A DURHAM

BOOK

Thomas Wright built this tower in 1711.
For what purpose? Answer on page 62.

Paul Perry

Illustrations by Helen Fenton

By the same author
Curiosities of County Durham (with Derek Dodds)
Portrait of Old Jarrow Vol 1
Portrait of Old Jarrow and Hebburn Vol 2

First published in 1998 by S. B. Publications,
c/o 19 Grove Road, Seaford, East Sussex BN25 1TP

ISBN 1 85770 179 8

Designed and typeset by CGB Lewes
Printed by MFP Design and Print
Longford Trading Estate, Thomas Street,
Stretford, Manchester M32 0JT

CONTENTS

Front cover: In what way has the historical importance of the Durham Cathedral and Castle been recognised by UNESCO?
Back cover: The eye window in St Edmund's church at Edmondbyers is there to ward off what?
(Answers on page 62)

INTRODUCTION

IT is all very well for the compilers of most quiz books – they know the answers before they ask the questions. But compilers of many county quiz books have a problem to solve before they start. What area is the book to cover?

Because of changes in the structure of local government, particularly the 1974 re-organisation, the counties are not what they were. Bits have been hived off to metropolitan authorities or been added to other counties and given a different name.

So it is with County Durham. Parts are now in Tyne and Wear, other parts in Cleveland. However, as far as this quiz book is concerned the changes have not happened. County Durham is as County Durham was from the days of the Prince Bishops.

This collection of memory joggers is neither complex nor daunting. It is quite simply a test of knowledge and recall – a what-do-you-know, what-don't-you-know about Durham, one of the most beautiful and historically fascinating counties in the country.

The questions and the answers are as informative as space permits and I sincerely hope you gain as much knowledge and pleasure from this quiz as I have in compiling it.

Paul Perry
Jarrow
October 1998

1 CASTLES AND FORTRESSES

*Hang out our banners on
the outward walls;
The cry is still, 'They come',
our castle's strength
Will laugh a siege to scorn.*

Macbeth Act V, scene v.

1 Of whom is Bishop Aukland Castle the official residence?

2 A twelfth century stone keep, built on the site of a Roman fort, guards the approach to Stainmore Pass. What is its name?

3 In which fourteenth century castle can you have an award-winning Elizabethan banquet?

4 This medieval castle with its 200 acre deer park has been home to Lord Barnard's family for more than 370 years.

5 What is the connection between a 500 years old stone carving of a shield on the tower of Hylton Castle and the Stars and Stripes?

6 Ludworth Tower was erected as a defence against whom?

7 The eighteenth century castellated house that is the 'castle' of Castle Eden was built for the first bearer of a name borne by five further members of the family. What is the name?

8 Lambton Castle was a former home of which 'ancient and honourable family'?

9 Who was the builder of the castle at Barnard Castle?

10 Which castle, with its massive 'chessmen' turrets, was for many years headquarters of the Durham Light Infantry.

2 SAINTS OF THE NORTH. . .

*Of course, before we know he is a saint, there will
have to be miracles.*

Graham Greene. *The Power and the Glory.*

1 Who was known as the Shepherd Saint?

2 Who was the hermit, later canonized, advised by St Cuthbert to build a shelter at Finchale, where he later died at the age of 105?

3 Relics of another Northern saint were in the coffin containing the body of St Cuthbert that the monks brought from Lindisfarne in 875. Which saint?

4 For the next 113 years the St Cuthbert's coffin rested in the wooden church built by the monks on a site close to a Roman fort. Where was the church?

5 Where are the remains of St Cuthbert now?

6 Who was the scholarly saint, author of *The Church History of the English People*, whose bones were stolen from Jarrow and brought to Durham *c* 1022.

7 After which saint is Romaldkirk named?

8 Who was known as the Apostle of the North?

9 And of which parish was he the rector from 1558 until his death in 1583?

10 A coal mine in South Shields was named after another of the northern saints. Which one?

3 . . . AND SINNERS

*The greatest saints and sinners have
been made,
The proselytes of one another's trade.*
Samuel Butler 1612-1680.
Miscellaneous Thoughts

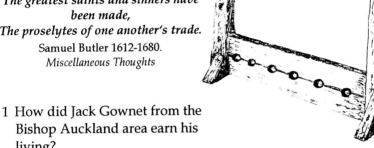

1 How did Jack Gownet from the
Bishop Auckland area earn his
living?

2 Mosstroopers were active in the wilds of the county in the
seventeenth and eighteenth centuries. What were they?

3 The Norman Bishop Walcher was murdered and his body
mutilated by an angry mob for condoning the murder of a Saxon
nobleman. Where did this eleventh century atrocity take place?

4 For what crime was the Venerable John Duckett of Wolsingham
executed at Tyburn on September 7, 1644?

5 Reader remember: Sleeping we were slain
And here we sleep till we must rise again
is part of the epitaph on the grave of three children murdered by
their father's servant in 1683. In which churchyard is it?

6 What did the widow of the Reverend John Garnage, rector of
Sedgefield, do to collect the tithes due a few days after his death?

7 Who was Dolly Peel?

8 Why is Galgate, a road at the top of the market place in Barnard
Castle, so called?

9 Name the former Sunday school teacher who was responsible
for fifteen murders in the nineteenth century.

10 Troops joined with police to put a security cordon round Durham
gaol for the arrival there, in 1967, of three convicted criminals.
Who were these Very Important Prisoners?

4 LIFE ON THE LAND

*Our farmers round, well pleased with
constant gain,
Like other farmers, flourish and complain.*

George Crabbe. *Baptisms*

1 Which Weardale village has the oldest agricultural show in England?

2 The home farm of the Beamish Hall estate has been restored. What award winning attraction is it now part of?

3 For what dairy product is the village of Cotherstone noted?

4 At his farm near Darlington Charles Colling bred an animal that gained world wide fame. What was it?

5 Limousins, Belgian Blues and Charollais can be seen in the pastures of upper Teesdale. What are they?

6 Botanists know them as the 'Teesdale Rarities'. What are they?

7 What beast of burden, a native of South America, is being bred successfully on a smallholding in Romaldkirk?

8 Why are all the farmhouses on the Raby estate at Laydon Beck whitewashed?

9 What is a Durham Argus?

10 There is a memorial to the inventor of the steam plough in South Park, Darlington. Who was he?

5 INDUSTRY

Man is a tool-making animal ...
Without tools he is nothing, with
tools he is all.

Thomas Carlyle. *Sartor Resartus.*

1 In which village, now a suburb of Darlington, was flax first spun by machinery?

2 The Consett Iron Company supplied the steel for the construction of one of the world's most famous bridges. Which one?

3 In what year did the giant steel works at Consett open?

4 And when did they close?

5 How many shipbuilding yards in Sunderland were producing ships in at the outbreak of the Second World War?

6 For centuries there was a bloomery in operation in the village of Evenwood. What is a bloomery?

7 What mining company, with a Quaker background, was the first in the country to introduce a five day week?

8 Where, in the county, has a steel making furnace been restored by English Heritage to its authentic eighteenth century state?

9 Eastgate, in Bishop Auckland, once boasted one of the world's largest works producing what?

10 The Wheel Mining Centre has a museum and working displays and memoribilia of lead mining. Where is the Centre?

6 SUNDERLAND FOOTBALL CLUB

Some people think football is a matter of life and death. I don't like that attitude. I can assure them it is much more serious than that.

Bill Shankly.
Sunday Times, October 4 1981

1 In what year was Sunderland Football Club formed?

2 Including the Stadium of Light, how many grounds has the club had?

3 'Stadium of Light' is also the name of the headquarters of another football team. Which one?

4 Sunderland have won the FA Cup on two occasions. In which years?

5 At the close of the 1997/8 season, how many points did the club have?

6 During the 1966 World Cup competition, how many games were played at Roker Park?

7 From whom did the club sign Marco Gabbiadini for £80,000 in 1987?

8 Sunderland's record attendance is 75,118. Against which club?

9 Who did the club play in its first, and last, games at Roker Park?

10 Who missed a penalty for Sunderland in the 1985 Milk Cup Final at Wembley?

7 MORE SPORTS

1 Which was the inaugural year of the Great North Run and who instigated it?

2 Where is the new Durham County Cricket Club ground?

3 In which track and field event does Jonathan Edwards compete?

4 Which is the only County Durham town to have a racecourse?

5 For which club did Steve Cram and David Sharpe run?

6 Who is the Formula One team boss who was born in South Shields and educated in Jarrow?

7 Which famous cricketer accepted the appointment of overseas patron of the Durham County Cricket Club in 1991?

8 Which County Durham boxer sparred more than 100 rounds with Mike Tyson?

9 How many British basketball titles did the former Sunderland team win?

10 Who was the former manager of England's football team born at Sacriston?

8 RAILWAYS

*You may threaten its life with a
railway share,
You may charm it with smiles
and soap.*

Lewis Carroll.
Through the Looking Glass.

1 Who, in 1813, built the locomotive known as 'Puffing Billy'?

2 What was the 'Marsden Rattler'?

3 Who was the Darlington Quaker mill-owner who used his wealth
and influence to support George Stephenson's railway projects?

4 Another founding father of the railways was Timothy Hackworth.
He built one of the first engines to be made. What was it called?

5 And what was the name of the works he established at Shildon in
1827?

6 On September 27 1825 the first train journey was made on the first
public railway in the world. From where to where?

7 And who was the engine driver?

8 What was the 'first' that gave Locomotion Number One its place
in railway history?

9 What is the name of the railway station at Beamish Museum?

10 Sunderland's Monkwearmouth station, now a museum, looks
more like a late Georgian country house. Who was the architect
who designed it?

9 GEORDIE DIALECT

Most of their discourse was about hunting, in a dialect I understood very little.

Samuel Pepys. *Diary, November 1663.*

1 What is a 'finnie haddy'?

2 What would you be if you were 'droothy'?

3 What is a fadge?

4 What would a 'colley' do for a living?

5 Where would you go to get 'scranchums'?

6 What is a shakedown?

7 What does 'jiggery pokery' mean?

8 What would a 'keeker' do for a living?

9 If someone is 'impittent' what would they be?

10 What are 'fernietickles'?

10 THE GEORDIE DICTIONARY

To make a dictionary is dull work.
Samuel Johnson.

1 'Kibosh' is an Irish word adopted by the Geordies. What does it mean?

2 The word 'hinnie' is used as a term of endearment, in the Geordie tongue, and is a corruption of another word. What is it?

3 The local word for a water closet is a shortened version of the word 'necessary'. What is it?

4 Almost every town and village in the county has a 'lonnen'. What is it?

5 Another corruption of this word is 'masacree'. Which word was it taken from?

6 What is 'haggismeat'?

7 What does 'gollop' mean?

8 'Ganzie' is a distortion of the word 'Guernsey'. What is it?

9 'Clamming' is another word used regularly. What does it mean?

10 What would you be doing if you were 'chuntering on'?

11 BRIDGES AND RIVER CROSSINGS

Standing on the bridge at midnight
She says: 'Farewell, blighted love'.
There's a scream, a splash – Good Heavens
What is she a-doing of?

Anonymous. *Poor But Honest*

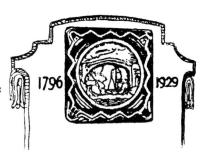

1 The original Wynch Bridge at Newbiggin in Teesdale, built in 1704, was said to be the first suspension bridge in Europe. What happened to it in 1820?

2 Who wrote the verse inscribed on a stone on the western approach to Prebends Bridge in Durham City?

3 In what year was the Tyne Bridge built?

4 Who was the designer of Causey Arch, the single span stone bridge over Beamish Burn?

5 What once stood in the centre of the two arched bridge at Barnard Castle?

6 In which village does a three arched bridge carry the former Roman Dere Street, now the B6275, across the Tees?

7 The Chain Bridge at Blaydon, mentioned in the the song *The Blaydon Races* was replaced in 1967 by a new bridge. What is it called.

8 How many bridges now link Gateshead with Newcastle?

9 In which year did the Tyne (road) Tunnel open?

10 This village, at one of the gateways to Teesdale, gets its name from the tributary of the Tees which was bridged there is 1771.

12 MONUMENTS AND MEMORIALS

Time, which antiquates antiquities, and hath an art to make dust of all things, hath yet spared these minor monuments.

Sir Thomas Browne, *Urn Burial.*

1 Who is the statesman depicted on the equestrian statue in the Market Place in Durham City?

2 What is heraldicly incorrect about the royal arms of George II in the church at Haughton-le-Skerne?

3 What statue stands on the top of the tall Doric column that coal magnate George Bowes had built on his Gibside estate around 1750?

4 Which American president's visit to Sunderland in 1877 is marked by an inscribed stone on the Central Libary and museum?

5 The first stage appearance of which famous actor – at Sunderland in 1856 – is marked by a bronze plaque in the same library?

6 Who is commemorated by the 127ft high obelisk on the Wynyard Park estate?

7 Who does the Penshaw Monument commemorate?

8 Fourteen effigies of supposedly medieval warriors were assembled by the seventh Lord Lambton as memorials to his illustratious ancestors. In which church are they?

9 Who designed the Angel of the North?

10 What form does the London Lead Company's tribute to one of its managers take at Middleton in Teesdale?

13 THE CITY QUIZ

*No city should be too large for a man to walk
out of in a morning.*

Cyril Connolly. *The Unquiet Grave*

1 When the monks arrived here in 995 with St Cuthbert's coffin the island hill on which they settled was not called Durham. What was it called?

2 Incorporated into the Victorian town hall is the city's oldest civic building. What is it?

3 Today Sherburn hospital is a residential home for the elderly. As what was it originally founded in 1181?

4 What commercial centre opened here in 1975?

5 Who gave Durham its first charter in 1178/80?

6 What did William Lloyd Wharton give to the city around 1860?

7 Several attempts were made to start a university at Durham. In what year was the Act of Parliament setting it up eventually passed?

8 For a time in 1650 Durham Cathedral served as a prison. For whom?

9 In what year did Durham's palatinate powers pass to the Crown?

10 What, in early Durham, were known as 'vennels'?

14 COAL MINING

He that diggeth a pit shall fall into it.
Ecclesiastes 10,8.

1 The formation in 1813 of the Sunderland Society for Preventing Accidents in Coal Mines, after a single pit explosion caused the death of ninety two miners, led to the invention of what safety device?

2 In what year was the coal industry nationalised?

3 Which was the first pit in the country to have pithead baths installed for the miners?

4 Why was wood used in preference to steel for pit props?

5 Why did Dawdon Colliery make the headlines in 1974?

6 What would a pitman do with 'hoggers'??

7 Prior to it being dismantled where was there a good example of a 'Kopje,' or 'Koefe' tower?

8 Where, in the city, was the first Durham Miners' Gala held?

9 Steel rope was used for the first time in the winding gear of this colliery where ninety five people lost their lives in 1844. Today only the remains of the machinery house still stands. Where?

10 A drift mine closed in 1958 has been re-opened as part of Beamish North of England Museum. What is the name of the mine?

15 THE CATHEDRAL AND ITS BISHOPS

Half house of God,
Half castle 'gainst the Scot.
Sir Walter Scott, *Harold the Dauntless*

1 The building of Durham Cathedral started in 1093. How long did it take to complete?

2 Where, on the cathedral, is the sanctuary knocker?

3 Who, in former years, was not allowed to cross the line of Frosterley marble in the floor to the east of the font in the cathedral?

4 Who was the bishop who converted the Norman manor house at Bishop Aukland into a castle?

5 Bishop Hugh Pudsey made a Domesday style survey of his 141 estates in 1183. What was it called?

6 To which Saxon bishop did King Alfred grant all the land between the Tyne and Tees?

7 Which bishop was three times Lord Chancellor of England?

8 Who is the present Bishop of Durham?

9 What is depicted in the Millenium Window of the cathedral?

10 Who was the post-Restoration bishop much given to beautifying the churches in his care?

16 TOWNS

Forget six counties overhung with smoke
Forget the snorting steam and piston stroke
Forget the spreading of the hideous town;
Think rather of the packhorse on the down.

William Morris. *The Wanderers.*

1 Seaham owes it existence to an aristocratic landowner's need for a port from which to ship his coal. Who was the landowner?

2 Where would you be if you were in 'Barney'?

3 The world's first Salvation Army band played in this industrial town in 1879.

4 After whom is the New Town of Peterlee named?

5 The county has two other New Towns. Which are they?

6 A Shrove Tuesday football match has been played on the green of this market town since the twelfth century.

7 Which town has a fossilised tree stump, believed to be 250 million years old, in a corner of its churchyard?

8 Which Durham town was formerly called Ceddersfield?

9 In one month, in 1849, a total of 143 inhabitants of Barnard Castle fell ill and died. What was the disease that killed them?

10 In the High Street of which town, now in Tyne and Wear, is Grimshaw's Elephant Tea House?

17 VILLAGES

1 What relic from the far past was placed on the green at Sadberge to commemorate Queen Victoria's golden jubilee?

2 'Elmyden Rawe,' is the ancient name for one of the villages in the county. What is it better known as?

3 In which hilltop village did astronomer and mathematician Thomas Wright, author of *Theory of the Universe*, set up an observatory in the mid-eighteenth century?

4 Where did another astronomer, the Reverend Thomas Espin, build his observatory and also design for the church a rood screen covered in acorns, fir cones, chestnuts and other tree seeds?

5 In the parish register of which village, near Stockton on Tees, is there an entry, made in 1752, about John Wright seeing fairies 'draped in green'.

6 Who is the dress designer of note who was brought up by his adoptive parents in the village of Hett?

7 Work by swordmakers from Solingen in Germany made this village famous in the seventeenth century?

8 Elizabeth Barrett Browning was born in this main road village – in a large house, now no more, rented by her parents.

9 Some mining villages have strange names. Why Pity Me?

10 And why Bearpark?

18 MUSEUMS

A cast of your skull, sir, until the original is available, would be an ornament to any anthropological museum.

Sir Arthur Conan Doyle. *His Last Bow.*

1 Which is the only museum in the country devoted entirely to Oriental art and antiquities?

2 Which museum holds both the British and European Museum of the Year awards?

3 A small folk museum stands next to an eighteenth century chapel where John Wesley preached. Which museum is it?

4 Who, in November 1869, laid the foundation stone of the magnificent Bowes Museum at Barnard Castle?

5 In which Durham museum can you see relics of St Cuthbert?

6 This museum was the former home and workplace of the superintendent engineer of the Stockton and Darlington Railway.

7 Durham Art Gallery shares premises with which museum?

8 And where was it previously?

9 Which building houses the Durham University Museum of Archeology?

10 What is featured in the Anker's House Museum at Chester-le-Street?

19 WHO? WHAT? WHEN? WHERE?

My advice to you is not to inquire the why or whither, but just enjoy your ice cream while it's on your plate. . .

Thornton Wilder. *The Skin of Our Teeth.*

1 In which year was the Jarrow March?

2 What is the 'Pitmens Derby'?

3 In which month does the annual Houghton Feast take place?

  4 When was the Battle of Neville's Cross fought?

5 Why is July 17 1983 significant to the residents of Irishopeburn in Durham?

6 Who was the Gateshead music hall performer who wrote the song *Blaydon Races* in 1862?

7 Who administered the blessing at the inauguration of the Stadium of Light?

8 Where in the county is the National Nature Reserve?

9 Who was known as 'King Jog' – for jogging along on £40,000 a year – and as 'Radical Jack'?

 10 Who was the king who built the first castle at Raby?

20 DURHAM BOOK OF RECORDS

'Twill be recorded for a precedent,
And many an error by the same example,
Will rush into the state.

William Shakespeare.
The Merchant of Venice.

1 What is the highest point in the county?

2 County Durham has the highest above ground waterfall in England. What is it called.

3 And what is its height?

4 Where is the highest stretch of main road in England?

5 What is Causey Arch's claim to fame?

6 Where is what is believed to be the world's oldest existing railway?

7 Which former Durham town boasts the widest street in the country?

8 What sporting event, the oldest of its kind in the country, is held each year in Durham City?

9 Which is the largest of Durham's coastal ravines?

10 Where is what is believed to be the oldest Methodist chapel in continuous use in the country?

21 CHURCHES AND CHAPELS

The Church's Restoration
In eighteen-eighty -three
Has left for contemplation
Not what there used to be.

Sir John Betjeman. *Hymn.*

1 What was the White Church?

2 Which church, built in 1907, is a veritable cathedral of the Arts and Crafts Movement, with work by Edward Burne Jones, William Morris, Ernest Gimson and Eric Gill?

3 Which Sunderland church is associated with the monastic life of the Venerable Bede?

4 St John the Evangelist at Escomb is one of the least altered Saxon churches in the country. How did it escape over-eager Victorian restorers?

5 St Andrew's church, in Dalton le Dale, has a most unusual sundial. What form does it take?

6 Which church is known as the Miners' Cathedral?

7 High House Chapel is the second oldest Methodist chapel in continuous use in the country. Where is it?

8 St Edmund's church at Edmundbyers, has an eye window built into the west wall. What was its purpose?

9 Where is the church that has the only detached bell-tower in the county?

10 In this Victorian church a block of granite from the Great Pyramid records that its tower and spire were given by Sir George Elliot MP. There is a similar block in another church where members of Sir George's family are buried. Name the churches?

22 LUCKY DIP

*They're always throwin' goodness
at you,
But with a little bit of luck
A man can duck!*

Alan Jay Lerner. *My Fair Lady*

1 The poem, *Maud*, was written at Brancepeth Castle. By whom?

2 Which President of the United States visited the county in the 1970s?

3 What was the primary function of Ushaw College?

4 At Ryhope there is one of the finest examples of Victorian engineering. What is it and what was its purpose?

5 Frosterly marble is not actually marble. What is it?

6 Above the door of which village inn can you see lead statues of a shepherd and shepherdess?

7 Where could you see a group of trees known as the 'Seven Sisters'?

8 What would you do with a 'Greenwell's Glory',

9 What is the A167 road through Durham better known as?

10 What was the emblem of the Durham Light Infantry?

23 FAMOUS MEN AND WOMEN

*Martyrdom is the only way in which a
man can become famous without ability.*

George Bernard Shaw. *Fabian Essays*

1 This best selling North Country
   novelist's maiden name was
   McMullen. What name appears on
   her books?

2 Robert Shafton lived at Whitworth Hall. By what name is he
   better known?

3 Lady Eden of Rushyford was also known by another name. What
   was it?

4 Who edited the *Northern Echo* at Darlington before going on to
   Fleet Street and fame – and making a last fatal voyage on the
   Titanic in 1912?

5 The line separating free America from the slave states of the south
   bears the name of this Cockfield-born Quaker who, with a
   colleague, surveyed it between 1763 and 1767.

6 Who, in the nineteenth century, was Durham's foremost
   architect?

7 This 'mad, bad and dangerous to know' Romantic poet made an
   unfortunate marriage at Seaham?

8 Actress Wendy Craig, was born in the county. Where?

9 Who was the developer responsible for the Metro Centre at
   Gateshead?

10 The church at Kelloe has a memorial to the birth in its parish of 'a
   great poetess, a noble woman, a devoted wife'. Who was she?

24 INNS

When you have lost your inns drown your empty selves, for you will have lost the last of England.

Hilaire Belloc. *This and That.*

1 The Eden Arms hotel at Rushyford is one of the county's oldest surviving coaching inns. What was its original name?

2 While staying at which hostelry in Barnard Castle did Charles Dickens collect material for *Nicholas Nickleby*?

3 J M Dent, publisher and founder of Everyman's Library was born in a Darlington inn. Which one?

4 What was unusual about the licensees of the Cross Keys Inn at Hamsterley?

5 The Duke of York at Fir Tree, Crook, has a unique collection of what?

6 Which public house had one of the five singing Smith brothers as its licensee?

7 Where in the county is there a public house hewn out of a rock face?

8 Which former football player became tenant of the Hastings Hill public house in Sunderland?

9 Which family of brewers set up the Castle Eden brewery in 1826?

10 Before it was licensed what was the Three Tuns public house at Sadberge?

25 LORE AND LEGEND

1 What was the 'Sockburn worm' with which Sir John Conyers did battle?

2 Another creature that terrorised the people, until killed by Sir Roger de Fery in the thirteenth century, was the Brawn of Brancepeth. What was it?

3 New Bishops of Durham still receive the Conyers Falchion on their first entry into the See. Where does this ceremony take place?

4 And what is the Conyers Falchion?

5 What is the relevance of the dun cow to Durham?

6 The story of the Lambton worm and its destruction is told in a Durham ballad. What does it say would happen to the family if Lord Lambton did not comply with all the conditions laid down by the witch who helped him slay the creature?

7 And where, according to the ballad, did Lambton 'hoy' the Fish?

8 What tradition is associated with weddings at the parish church of Romaldskirk?

9 Who is said to haunt the ramparts of Raby Castle, knitting with red hot needles?

10 Where is a battle of two giants marked by a cairn of stones?

26 FOLLIES AND FINE HOUSES

The stately homes of England,
How beautiful they stand,
To prove the upper classes,
Have still the upper hand.

Sir Noël Coward. *Operette.*

1 Who are the present occupants of Biddick Hall, near Chester le Street?

2 And who is at Wynyard Hall?

3 Bishop Trevor had a large turreted structure built at Bishop Auckland in 1767. For what purpose?

4 Windlestone Hall, near Ferryhill, was the birthplace, in this century of a former British Prime Minister. Who?

5 Unthank Hall stands close to the River Wear. Why is it so named?

6 What unusual feature has Ornsby Hill House, at Lanchester?

7 What physical link is there between Hamsterley Hall, childhood home of Dunkirk hero, Field Marshal Viscount Gort VC, and the Mother of Parliaments?

8 Redworth Hall near Bishop Auckland, is associated with the Surtees family. For what purpose is it used today?

9 Where, in 1876, did industrialist William Wailes built the Tudor cum Gothic architectural extravaganza, Saltwell Towers?

10 A little Doric folly, designed by Joseph Bonomie on the bank of the Wear in Durham City, is known locally as the Count's House. Who was the Count and what was special about him?

27 ROMAN REMAINS

The Roman Conquest was, however, a **Good Thing.**

W C Sellar and R J Yeatman.
1066 and All That.

1 When Binchester was a Roman fort what was its name?

2 Where can you visit one of the finest examples of a Roman hypocaust found in England?

3 The hypocaust was discovered accidentally in 1815. How?

4 What tribe formed the native population of Durham when it was under Roman rule?

5 What did the Romans do to the Tees near Piercebridge to facilitate the transport of goods?

6 One of the largest Roman camps in Britain – it covers eleven acres – is under the green in which village?

7 What did Bishop Egelric do with the hoard of Roman gold found in 1080 when a new church was being built at Chester-le-Street?

8 In Roman times what was the 'Street' of Chester-le-Street?

9 What was the name of the Roman fort built to guard the Derwent river crossing at Ebchester?

10 Little now remains to be seen here of *Longovicium,* the long fort of the Roman occupation. Where?

28 MISCELLANEOUS

On Monday when the sun is hot,
I wonder to myself a lot,
'Now is it true or is it not
That what is which and which is what'

A A Milne. *Winnie the Pooh.*

1 Soon after the death in 1834 of the author of *Jorrocks* the Surtees Society was formed. For what purpose?

2 In which church is there a Wurlitzer organ?

3 Name the reservoir formed by the dam that holds back the head waters of the Tees?

4 What brought the oddly-named Middleton One Row into existence?

5 Where is Tees-side Airport?

6 What was the name of the Durham Ice Hockey team?

7 Name the forest that covers 5,000 acres of the Durham moors?

8 How many times, according to the ballad, did the Lambton worm wrap its tail round Penshaw Hill?

9 What are The Castles at Bedburn?

10 Where was the school, used by Dickens as a model for Dotheboys Hall, that had to close after the publication of *Nicholas Nickleby*?

29 COUNTY PICTURE QUIZ

1 This ancient gothic gatehouse dates from 1764. Where is it?

2 For what was this odd shaped building at Hall Garth, Coatham Mundeville used?

3   This fine octagonal building from 1747 is in the centre of Barnard Castle. What were its principle uses?

4 This column is all that remains of the market cross erected by Bishop John Cosin in 1669 to mark the re-founding of an earlier charter fair. Where is it now?

5 Where is this statue of strongman John English?

6   This battlemented and pinnacled gateway was built by Bishop Trevor in 1760. To what does it form the gateway?

7 What is this strange looking object on the lawn at Lumley Castle?

8   Where would you go to visit this clock museum?

9   What is the name of this magnificent medieval castle?

10 Which famous Durham legend is depicted by this statue?

30 CITY PICTURE QUIZ

1   What is the name commonly given to this area in front of the cathedral?

2   What is the name of this city river crossing?

3 What is the name of this church in the market place at Durham?

4 Another building in the marketplace. What is it?

5 Where is this statue of Neptune?

6 Where are these tree trunks, carved by the cathedral's artist in residence Colin Wilbourn in 1986/87, on display?

7 A part of Durham Castle – but what part?

8 Above a shop in which street is the teapot?

9 On what building are these armorial bearings?

45

10 A somewhat ornate structure for a practical purpose. What is it?

ANSWERS

1 CASTLES AND FORTRESSES

1 The Bishop of Durham.

2 Bowes Castle. Its walls are still standing and the site is maintained by English Heritage.

3 Lumley Castle at Chester-le-Street. It is now an hotel.

4 Raby Castle, near Staindrop. It was in the possession of the Nevilles until the failure of the Rising of the North led to this proud family's disgrace.

5 The shield bears the arms of ancestors of George Washington. They appear as three stars and two stripes and from them, according to tradition, came the Stars and Stripes.

6 The Scots.

7 Rowland Burdon. They were lords of the manor from 1758.

8 The Earls of Durham.

9 Guy de Baliol. The site was given to him by William Rufus at the end of the eleventh century.

10 Brancepeth.

2 NORTHERN SAINTS. . .

1 St Cuthbert.

2 St Godric.

3 St Aidan, founder of the monastery on Lindisfarne.

4 At Chester-le-Street.

5 Durham Cathedral

6 The Venerable Bede.

7 St Rumwald, who built the church there in Anglo Saxon times.

8 Bernard Gilpin, a saintly divine who devoted his life to the service of his fellow men.

9 Houghton-le-Spring, where he founded a grammar school and kept open house for the poor in the rectory.

10 St Hilda. She was King Edwin's great niece and abbess of religious houses at Whitby and Hartlepool.

3 . . . AND SINNERS

1 He was a highwayman.

2 Marauders who plundered the farms of the Scottish borders, stealing cattle and whatever else they could carry off.

3 The bishop was in council in St Mary's church, Gateshead, which was burnt by the mob.

4 For being a priest – a hanging matter in the days of religious intolerance before the Restoration.

5 In Kirk Merrington churchyard are buried the bodies of John, Jane and Elizabeth Brass.

6 Pickled him in salt and placed his body at the window so parishioners would not realise their rector was dead.

7 A notorious smuggler from South Shields.

8 It is where the gallows stood.

9 Mary Ann Cotton.

10 Three of the Great Train Robbers.

4 LIFE ON THE LAND

1 Woolsingham.

2 The North of England Open Air Museum.

3 Cheese.

4 The Durham Ox, father of the dairying variety of the Shorthorn breed throughout the world.

5 Breeds of cattle.

6 Arctic alpine and mountain plants like spring gentians and cinquefoil, that have grown in Upper Teesdale since climate changes melted the ice sheets of the last glaciation.

7 The llama.

8 On the orders of Lord Barnard who, when lost in the fog while out shooting, was turned away from the farmhouse from which he sought help because it was not his property.

9 A butterfly of the Brown Argus family.

10 John Fowler, 1826–64.

5 INDUSTRY

1 At Haughton-le-Skerne by mill owner, John Kendrew.

2 Sydney Harbour bridge.

3 In 1840

4 In 1980.

5 Four.

6 A furnace for producing malleable iron.

7 The London Lead Company.

8 At Derwentcote, near Rowlands Gill.

9 Cement.

10 At Killhope in Upper Weardale.

6 SUNDERLAND FOOTBALL CLUB

1 In 1879.

2 Seven.

3 Benfica.

4 In 1937 and 1973.

5 Ninety.

6 Four.

7 York City.

8 Derby County.

9 Liverpool.

10 Clive Walker.

7 MORE SPORTS

1 It was inaugurated by Brendan Foster in 1981.

2 At Chester-le-Street.

3 Triple Jump.

4 Sedgefield.

5 Jarrow and Hebburn.

6 Frank Williams.

7 Sir Donald Bradman.

8 Glenn McCory.

9 Two. In 1981 and in 1983.

10 Bobby Robson.

8 RAILWAYS

1 Railway pioneer William Hedley of Burnhopeside Hall. The engine was first known as 'Wylam Dilly', and was built to haul coal from Wylam Colliery to a pierhead on the Tyne.

2 A locomotive which operated from Whitburn to South Shields.

3 Edward Pease, born 1787. He was a member of a Darlington family of industrialists renowned for their devotion to good causes.

4 Sans Pareil.

5 The Soho Engineering Works.

6 From Shildon to Darlington and then on to Stockton.

7 The great George Stephenson himself.

8 It was the first steam locomotive to run on a public railway.

9 Rowley.

10 John Dobson of Newcastle.

9 GEORDIE DIALECT

1 Smoked Haddock.

2 Thirsty.

3 A small flat loaf of bread.

4 A colley was a lamplighter.

5 Fish and chip shop.

6 A temporary bed on the floor.

7 Underhanded dealings.

8 Inspect the coal's as they come from the pit.

9 Cheeky.

10 Freckles.

10 THE GEORDIE DICTIONARY

1 A finishing touch.

2 Honey.

3 Netty.

4 A lane.

5 Massacre.

6 Minced tripe.

7 To eat hastily.

8 A close fitting woollen shirt.

9 Very hungry

10 Grumbling or muttering imprecations under one's breath.

11 BRIDGES AND RIVER CROSSINGS

1 It collapsed as nine people were walking across it. One man fell to his death into the river below.

2 Sir Walter Scott.

3 1928.

4 Ralph Wood.

5 A chapel.

6 Piercebridge.

7 Scotswood Bridge.

8 Six.

9 1967.

10 Greta Bridge, Greta being the name of the tributary.

12 MONUMENTS AND MEMORIALS

1 The 3rd Marquis of Londonderry.

2 They show the quarterings of the Stuarts, not the Hanovers.

3 The British Liberty.

4 General Ulysses S Grant who was on a world tour after his second term as president.

5 Sir Henry Irving.

6 The Duke of Wellington, victor of Waterloo.

7 John George Lambton, 1st Earl of Durham

8 In the Church of St Mary and St Cuthbert at Chester-le-Street.

9 Anthony Gormley sculpted this 65ft high steel structure with its 175ft wingspan. It stands by the A1 at Gateshead, marking the southern entrance to Tyneside.

10 The cast iron-canopied Bainbridge drinking fountain in the main street.

13 CITY QUIZ

1 Dunholm.

2 The fourteenth century Guildhall.

3 A leper colony.

4 The Milburngate shopping centre.

5 Bishop Middleham.

6 The land that forms Wharton Park.

7 In 1832.

8 For 4,000 Scots captured at the Battle of Dunbar. They destroyed a lot of its woodwork to keep warm in the winter.

9 In 1836.

10 The narrow lanes leading down to the river Wear.

14 COAL MINING

1 The miner's lamp.

2 In 1947.

3 Boldon Pit, in 1927.

4 Because any weakness in them would be indicated by the creaking of the wood.

5 The world's first tunnelling machines were installed there.

6 He would wear them. They are footless stockings.

7 Murton Colliery.

8 Wharton Park.

9 Haswell Plough.

10 Mahogany mine

15 THE CATHEDRAL AND ITS BISHOPS

1 Forty years.

2 On the great north doorway which dates from ther twelfth century.

3 Women. They were not allowed to approach any closer to the altar in monastic churches.

4 Bishop Anthony Bek, 1283–1311.

5 The *Boldon Book* as, after the inital entry under Boldon, many of the subsequent entries simply state: 'in all respects like Boldon'.

6 The Saxon Bishop Eardulph.

7 Bishop Thomas Langley. He was also a royal ambassador and helped negotiate the Treaty of Troyes, which made Henry V Regent and heir to the throne of France.

8 Michael Turnbull.

9 A thousand year history of Durham.

10 Bishop John Cosin.

16 TOWNS

1 The 3rd Marquis of Londonderry, owner of Rainton colliery.

2 Barnard Castle.

3 Consett.

4 Peter Lee, 1864–1935. He started work in the pits at the age of ten and rose to become President of the International Federation of Miners.

5 Newton Aycliffe and Washington.

6 Sedgefield. The game dates from the twelfth century and can last for hours.

7 Stanhope. The trunk, believed to be 250 million years old, was found during quarrying at Edmundbyers Cross.

8 Sedgefield.

9 Asiatic cholera, according to the inscription on the cross beside an avenue of limes in the churchyard.

10 Sunderland. Frank Caws, who designed the building, planned to turn Fawcett Street into an Indian style thoroughfare.

17 VILLAGES

1 A boulder from the Ice Age, found 12ft below the ground during the making of a reservoir.

2 Helminton Row.

3 Westerton.

4 At Tow Law, in the garden of the vicarage.

5 Bishopton.

6 Bruce Oldfield.

7 Shotley Bridge. Sword making continued here until well into the nineteenth century.

8 She was born in 1806 at Coxhoe Hall in Coxhoe.

9 It derives from *petit mere,* a small lake. One existed here in the distant past.

10 There are no bears about. It is a corruption of *beau repaire,* as the medieval priors of Durham called their country retreat here.

18 MUSEUMS

1 Durham University Oriental Museum, Elvet Hill, off South Road in Durham City.

2 Beamish: North of England Open Air Museum.

3 The Weardale Museum at Ireshopeburn.

4 Josephine Bowes, who before her marriage was the French actress and artist, Josephine Benoite, Countess of Montalba. Both she and her husband, the illegitimate son of the 10th Earl of Strathmore, had died before the museum was opened in 1892.

5 Durham Cathedral's Treasury Museum. It has the saint's coffin, his pectoral cross, embroidered stole and other relics.

6 Timothy Hackworth Victorian and Railway Museum at Shildon.

7 The Durham Light Infantry Museum which traces the history of the county regiment from 1758 to 1968 when it was disbanded.

8 Brancepeth Castle.

9 The Old Fulling Mill in Durham City.

10 How an anchorite, walled up for life, passed the time in prayer and meditation.

19 WHO? WHAT? WHEN? WHERE?

1 In October 1936.

2 The Northumberland Plate. A sixteen furlong race run at Newcastle.

3 In October, usually between October 3 and October 10.

4 On October 17 1346.

5 A terrific storm devasted the village.

6 Geordie Ridley.

7 The Bishop of Durham, the Rt Reverend Michael Turnbull.

8 At Langdon Beck in Upper Teesdale.

9 John George Lambton, 1st Earl of Durham, statesman and Governor General of Canada. He established a Benevolent Association for old and ill miners in his collieries.

10 King Cnut (or Canute) who reigned from 1017 to 1036.

20 THE DURHAM BOOK OF RECORDS

1 Pontop Pike, St Johns Chapel.

2 High Force at Langdon Beck.

3 Seventy feet.

4 At Killhope Cross. It is 2,056ft above sea level.

5 It is the oldest stone railway bridge in the world.

6 The Tanfield Railway at Old Marley Hill, near Stanley, first opened in 1725 with horses pulling coal waggons along wooden rails.

7 Stockton on Tees, now in Cleveland. An open air market, started in 1310, was held twice weekly in its High Street.

8 The Durham Regatta.

9 Castle Eden Dene.

10 Newbiggin Methodist Chapel

21 CHURCHES AND CHAPELS

1 The first church built by the monks who brought St Cuthbert's coffin and relics to the island hill of Dunholm. It was dedicated in 998.

2 St Andrew's, Roker, in seaside Sunderland,

3 St Peter's. It is all that survives of the monastery, founded by Benedict Biscop in 675 as a sister house to the one at Jarrow.

4 They decided to build a new church higher up the hill. This has since been demolished and the Saxon one sensitively restored.

5 It is on the north wall inside the church and the sun's rays reach it through the window opposite.

6 St Mary's church, Horden.

7 Ireshopeburn.

8 To ward off evil spirits.

9 At Middleton in Teesdale It was built to hold the three bells bequeathed to the parish by the Reverend William Bell in the the early seventeenth century.

10 St Mary's, West Rainton and All Saints' at Penshaw.

22 LUCKY DIP

1 Alfred, Lord Tennyson.

2 Jimmy Carter.

3 It was a Roman Catholic seminary founded by Bishop Allen in 1568 and was originally based at Douai. After the French Revolution it came to Crook Hall, near Stanley and then to Bearpark in 1808.

4 The Ryhope Pumping Station, built to lift water from below ground to supply the drinking water requirements of the area.

5 Limestone speckled with thousands of little fossils

6 On the Shepherd and Shepherdess at Beamish. They were originally in the grounds of Beamish Hall but were given to the inn, so it is said, in 1870 by the squire. He had bumped into one of them when returning home slightly the worse for drink, and thought it was a ghost.

7 Copt Hill, Houghton le Spring.

8 Attach it to a fishing line. It is an artificial fly.

9 The Great North Road.

10 A crown from which depends a bugle bearing the initials DLI.

23 FAMOUS MEN AND WOMEN

1 Catherine Cookson.

2 Bobby Shafto.

3 Lady Bountiful – for she was a kind and generous woman who gave to the poor in days when few others did.

4 W T Stead.

5 Jeremiah Dixon. He surveyed the boundary with Charles Mason – hence the Mason-Dixon Line.

6 Ignatius Bonomi.

7 Lord Byron.

8 At Sacriston.

9 Sir John Hall. He was chairman of Newcastle United Football Club and rose from humble beginnings to become one of the wealthiest men on Tyneside.

10 Elizabeth Barrett Browning

24 INNS

1 The Wheatsheaf.

2 The King's Head.

3 The Britannia Inn in Bondgate.

4 It was run by an order of monks.

5 Pipes.

6 The Ship Inn, Heworth, Gateshead.

7 The Marsden Grotto, South Shields.

8 Bobby Kerr.

9 The Nimmos. Their brewery was originally built as a corn mill.

10 A court house.

25 LORE AND LEGEND

1 A dragon or 'fiery flying serpent'.

2 A wild boar.

3 Originally at Neasham Ford on their entry to the diocese. Later on Croft Bridge when it was built to provide a drier crossing of the Tees at this point.

4 The sword with which Sir John slew the serpent.

5 The monks carrying St Cuthbert's coffin where led to its final resting place by a girl seeking her dun cow.

6 Nine generations of Lambtons would not die in their beds.

7 'Doon the well'.

8 The groom must throw coins over the gate for it to be opened.

9 Elizabeth, wife of the first Lord Barnard. She was known as the Old Hell Cat and she and her husband virtually stripped the castle bare and killed off the deer in the park in a rage over their eldest son's choice of a wife.

10 On Pawlaw Pike at Bollihope. Villagers heard the fight in the night and next day found the body of a huge man which they hastily buried where it lay.

26 FOLLIES AND FINE HOUSES

1 Lord and Lady Lambton.

2 Sir John and Lady Hall.

3 As a shelter for deer. Its tower was used for hunting parties.

4 Sir Anthony Eden, later Lord Avon.

5 The name derives from the Old English words meaning 'without leave', a hint, perhaps, that there were once squatters here.

6 It has a well inside the house.

7 A minaret removed from the Houses of Parliament when they were being restored in the 1930s was acquired by Lord Gort's brother and stands on the terrace on front of the house.

8 As an hotel and conference centre.

9 In Saltwell Park, Gateshead.

10 Count Joseph Boruwlaski, a 3ft 3ins tall Polish aristocrat and talented violinist. He died in Durham City in 1837, aged ninety nine, and is buried in the cathedral.

27 ROMAN REMAINS

1 *Vinovia*, meaning 'a pleasant spot'.

2 At Binchester.

3 A wall of the ruined room above it was struck by a plough and collapsed to reveal the central heating system below.

4 Brigantes.

5 They built a canal alongside a length of it.

6 Piercebridge.

7 Took it back with him to Peterborough and spent it on building new roads through the Fens.

8 Dere Street, the Roman's link road from Hadrian's wall to York.

9 *Vindomora*.

10 At Lanchester.

28 MISCELLANEOUS

1 The publication of historical manuscripts dealing with the North of England.

2 Howden le Wear.

3 Cow Green reservoir.

4 The discovery in the early nineteenth century of sulphur spring at Low Dinsdale. A row of houses were built to accommodate Victorian visitors keen to sample the waters of the new spa.

5 At Middleton St George.

6 The Wasps.

7 Hamsterley Forest.

8 Ten times.

9 An earthwork of unknown date surrounded by trees.

10 At Bowes. The house stands back from the A66 at the western end of the village.

29 COUNTRY PICTURE QUIZ

1 Hardwick Hall Country Park.

2 It is a refuge for deer.

3 It was the town hall and court house

4 In the churchyard at Stanhope.

5 At Whickham.

6 Auckland Castle.

7 A sundial.

8 At Whitworth Hall.

9 Raby Castle.

10 The slaying of the Lambton worm.

30 CITY PICTURE QUIZ

1 Palace Green.

2 Framwellgate Bridge.

3 St Nicholas.

4 The Town Hall.

5 Since the eighteenth century it has stood in various locations in the market place.

6 Beneath Prebends Bridge on the Riverside.

7 The castle keep.

8 Saddler Street.

9 On the former exchequer and chancery of the Palatine, on Palace Green, now the university library.

10 A water tower.

LIST OF LINE DRAWINGS ON RELATED SUBJECTS

ANSWERS TO COVER AND TITLE PAGE QUESTIONS

Front cover: It has been designated a World Heritage Site.

Title page: As an observatory.

Back cover: To ward off evil spirits and as a protection against witches.

ACKNOWLEDGEMENTS

I am most grateful to the following people and organisations for their assistance with the questions and answers for this book:
The staff at the Local History Departments of Newcastle and South Tyneside libraries; Angela, Anthony and Kelly Perry; the Friends of Durham Cathedral; and particular thanks to Jeff Pease for his invaluable assistance.

BIBLIOGRAPHY

Companion Guide to Northumbria by Edward Grierson. Collins 1976.

County Durham, A Shell Guide by Henry Thorold. Faber and Faber 1980.

Curiosities of County Durham by Paul Perry and Derek Dodds. S. B. Publications 1996.

The King's England – Durham by Arthur Mee. Hodder and Stoughton 1969.

The New Shell Guides. North-East England by Brian Spencer. Shell Publication 1988.

Fact Sheets: *The Prince Bishops of County Durham, Industrial Heritage; Durham Cathedral.* Durham County Council Marketing and Promotion 1998.

The Durham Quiz Book is the latest in a series of county quiz books published by

S. B. Publications
**c/o 19 Grove Road,
Seaford,
East Sussex BN25 1TP**

Quiz books, priced at £4.99, are also available for the following counties:

Bedfordshire
Cambridgeshire
Dorset
Gloucestershire
Herefordshire
Leicestershire
Norfolk
Northamptonshire
Oxfordshire
Suffolk
Surrey
Sussex
Warwickshire
Worcestershire.

THE QUIZ BOOKS ARE AVAILABLE FROM BOOKSHOPS OR DIRECTLY FROM THE PUBLISHERS AT THE PRICE STATED, PLUS £1 FOR POSTAGE AND PACKING. PLEASE MAKE CHEQUES PAYABLE TO S. B. PUBLICATIONS AND SEND TO THE ABOVE ADDRESS.